D0831299

Mind-Bending
Time-Critical Puzzles

Editor: Colleen Collier

Puzzle Compilator: Lloyd King, Rich Garner

Additional Contributors: Sarah Wells, Peter Sorenti,
Jane Purcell, Sue Curran

Page Layout & Design: Linley Clode

Cover Design: Gary Inwood Studios

Published by:
LAGOON BOOKS
PO BOX 311, KT2 5QW, UK
PO Box 990676, Boston, MA 02199, USA

www.lagoongames.com

ISBN 1-902813-48-0

© LAGOON BOOKS, 2001.

Lagoon Books is a trademark of
Lagoon Trading Company Limited.
All rights reserved.

All rights reserved. No part of this publication
may be reproduced, stored in a retrieval system,
or transmitted in any form or by any other means,
electronic, mechanical, photocopying or otherwise,
without prior permission in writing from the publisher.

Printed in Singapore.

Mind-Bending
Time-Critical Puzzles

LAGOON
BOOKS

INTRODUCTION

Engage your brain and test the old gray matter against the clock with this stunning collection of time-critical puzzles.

All the Mind-Bending puzzle books have been carefully compiled to give the reader a refreshingly wide range of challenges, some requiring only a small leap of perception, others deep and detailed thought. All the books share an eye-catching and distinctive style that presents each problem in an appealing and intriguing way. And this one features a battle against the clock! Keep a stopwatch close to hand and see if you can crack the conundrums within the one, two, or three-minute time limits allowed.

Have you got what it takes?

OTHER TITLES AVAILABLE FROM LAGOON

MIND-BENDING PUZZLE BOOKS

Mind-Bending Sports Puzzles
(1-902813-51-0)
Mind-Bending Cryptogram Puzzles
(1-902813-49-9)
Mind-Bending Lateral & Logic Puzzles
(1-902813-50-2)
Mind-Bending Lateral Thinking Puzzles
(1-89971-206-2)
More Mind-Bending Lateral Thinking Puzzles
(1-89971-219-4)
Mind-Bending Challenging Optical Puzzles
(1-89971-269-0)
Mind-Bending Maze Puzzles
(1-89971-272-0)
Mind-Bending Conundrums and Puzzles
(1-89971-203-8)
Mind-Bending Lateral Thinking Puzzles by Des MacHale
(1-89971-223-2)
Mind-Bending Classic Logic Puzzles
(1-89971-218-6)
Mind-Bending Challenging Logic Puzzles
(1-89971-224-0)

ONE MINUTE PUZZLES

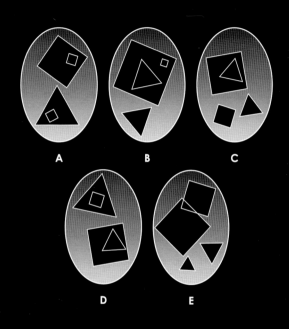

In which of these eggs can you place a dot so that it is in two squares and a triangle?

Five reserve players for the Fulchester Falcons football team are sitting on the sidelines. Their shirts are numbered with consecutive digits. Player Smith is called into play, reducing the total of the numbers on the shirts by one-sixth. What was the number on Player Smith's shirt?

ONE MINUTE

Six equilateral triangles can be assembled to make a hexagon and four squares can be assembled to make another square. So what regular figure does six of the following shape (made up of a square and two equilateral triangles) make?

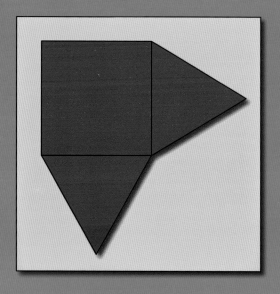

ONE MINUTE

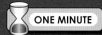

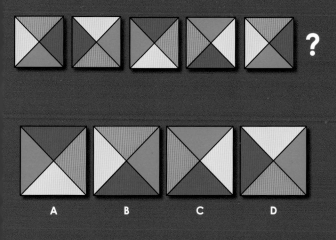

C ontinue the colored sequence and work out which of options A to D is the missing square.

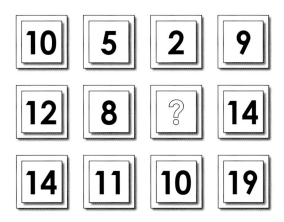

What is the missing number in this grid?

Can you determine the values of the three hidden numbers?

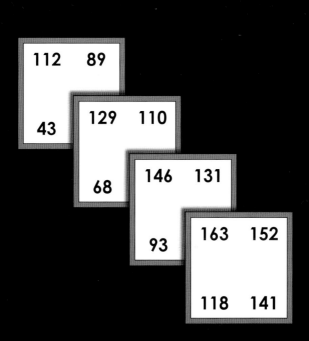

112 89

43

129 110

68

146 131

93

163 152

118 141

ONE MINUTE

Complete the sequence from one of the following options. (Note – it will be far easier to work out if you use a piece of paper and a pen).

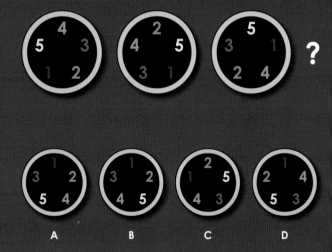

A   B   C   D

ONE MINUTE

Can you rearrange these letters to create a familiar letter series?

$$3526 = 9$$

Add four toothpicks to make this equation correct. But you have to solve it first!

These figures are not just random squiggles designed to frustrate and annoy. What are they and what will the next figure in the sequence be?

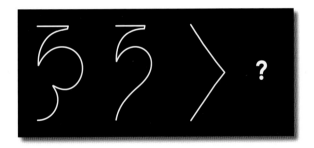

Complete this bar chart sequence from the options shown.

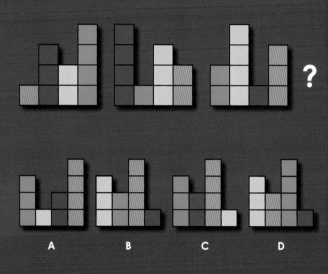

?

A   B   C   D

ONE MINUTE

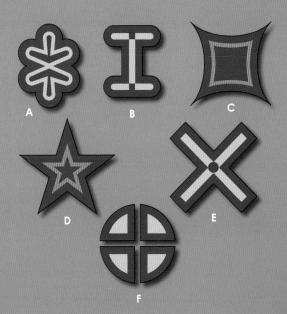

A

B

C

D

E

F

Which of these shapes is the odd one out?

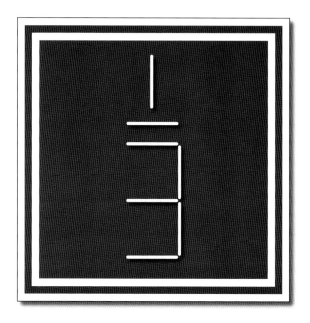

Add a toothpick to leave an eighth and also a ninth.

Fill in the missing numbers. To obtain the numbers on the left-hand side, multiply the two touching squares. To obtain the numbers on the right-hand side, divide the higher touching square by the lower touching square. Only use whole numbers, and note that the numbers can be repeated.

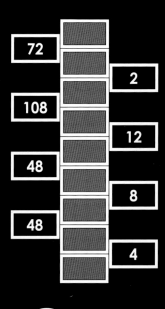

72

2

108

12

48

8

48

4

ONE MINUTE

C an you complete the sequence with one of the
following images?

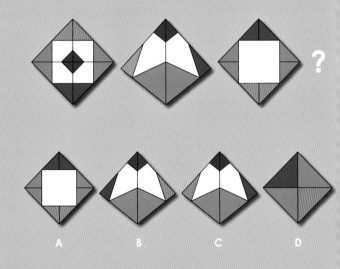

A   B   C   D

ONE MINUTE

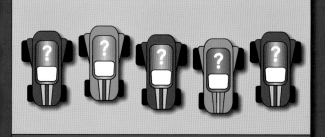

Five racing cars are waiting on the starting grid. Each car is numbered with a consecutive two-digit figure. Car X is left behind at the starting line after stalling, reducing the total of the numbers by one-sixth. What was Car X's number?

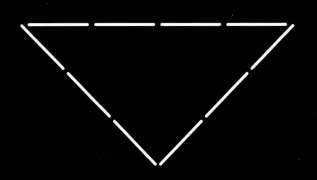

Add two more toothpicks to this triangle to leave a number.

Maria has three gorgeous puppies called Tigger, Spot and Rory. But she wants another one. Will she choose Pauly, Quentin, or Rosie?

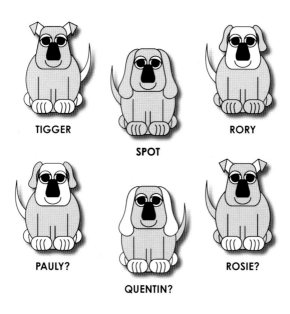

TIGGER

SPOT

RORY

PAULY?

QUENTIN?

ROSIE?

ONE MINUTE

Which of these teapots is the odd one out?

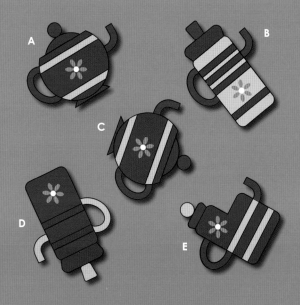

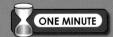

ONE MINUTE

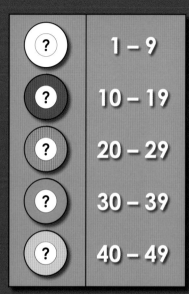

?	1 – 9
?	10 – 19
?	20 – 29
?	30 – 39
?	40 – 49

The National Lottery balls are numbered as shown. The six jackpot balls drawn are arranged in ascending numerical order and appear as a palindrome (i.e. they read the same backwards as forwards). All five colors are present – what is the number on the green ball?

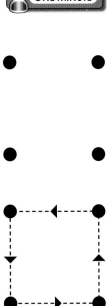

As you can see, it is possible to draw four straight lines through the dots without taking pen from paper. Can you do the same, however, with only three straight lines?

From the options shown, work out what the second shape is equal to.

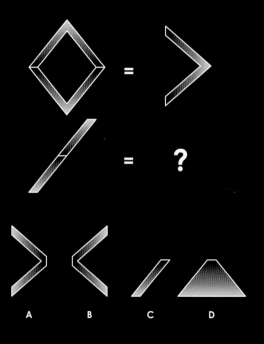

ONE MINUTE

If 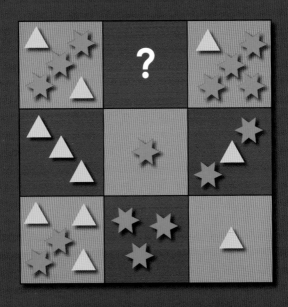 = 5 and ⭐ = 1, what should fill the missing square?

ONE MINUTE

O	J	A	I	L	G
P	X	P	V	Y	Z
G	H	T	E	P	O

Which two farmyard animals are indicated by X and Y?

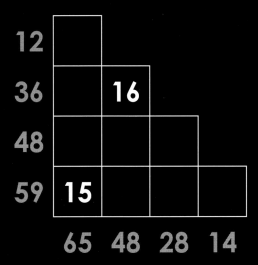

Place the digits 11 to 20 (with 15 and 16 as shown) in the boxes so that they add to the totals shown against each row and column.

Arrange these tiles to form a number square so that the same five numbers that appear in Row 1 also appear in the same order as Column 1, the same numbers that appear in Row 2 also appear in Column 2, etc.

| 9 | 7 | |

| 6 |
| 5 |
| 4 |

| 4 |
| 1 |

| 2 |
| 3 |
| 5 |

| 7 |
| 2 |

| 8 |
| 6 |

| 9 | 2 | 3 |

| 6 |
| 4 |
| 8 |

| 1 |
| 6 |

| 7 | 3 | 4 |

ONE MINUTE

Polly was studying the stained glass windows of her local church when she suddenly realized that they followed a sequence. Which of the options shown should be next?

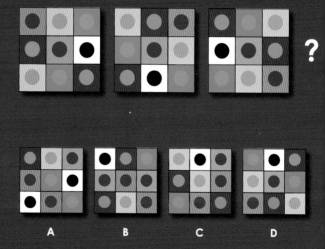

A   B   C   D

ONE MINUTE

TWO MINUTE PUZZLES

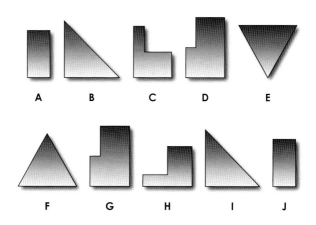

A B C D E

F G H I J

Which pair of identical shapes shown are the odd ones out and why?

Continue this sequence of adjoining squares from one of the options shown.

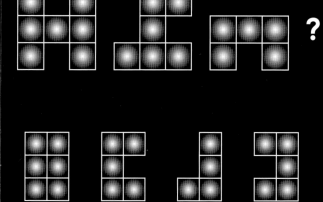

?

The red knights of Laguna always tell the truth and the blue knights of Laguna always lie. Five knights are sitting around a circular table and when asked, 'Is there at least one red guard sitting next to you?' they all answered 'No'. How many red guards were sitting at the table?

TWO MINUTE

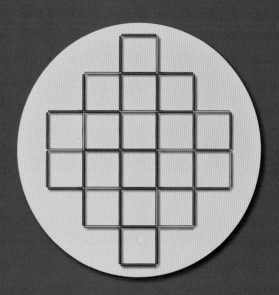

Here are some toothpicks arranged to create 18 small squares. Without changing the overall shape, can you take 5 away to leave 13 small squares?

C an you turn this unfinished rectangular puzzle into a completed square?

C an you solve this pentagonal problem and determine the missing number?

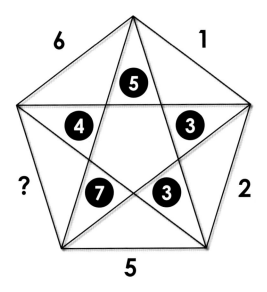

Clunk the robot must reach the red area in the center of the arena. When he passes through two yellow walls, he's programmed to turn right. When he passes through two blue walls, he turns left. When he passes through a yellow and blue wall, he goes straight on. Which entrance will allow him to succeed?

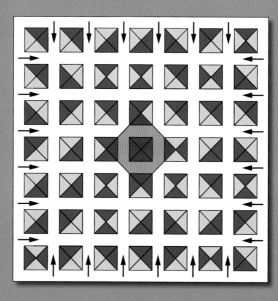

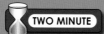

TWO MINUTE

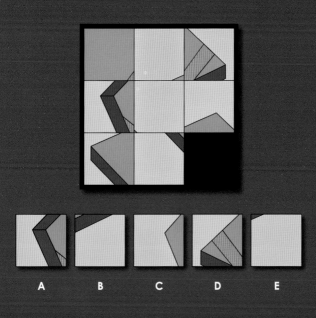

A   B   C   D   E

Of the five options shown, what is the missing tile that will complete the pattern?

15, 30, 40, 45, 55, 60, ?

There is only one more number needed to complete
this sporting sequence (which may not always occur in
the order you see). Can you work out what comes next?

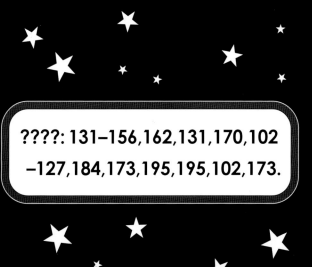

Each three-digit number represents a letter. Decode them and the question marks become a famous film title that's out of this world!

????: 131–156,162,131,170,102 –127,184,173,195,195,102,173.

TWO MINUTE

Sarah has forgotten the combination needed to unlock her briefcase. The combination code is made up of a specific sequence using four symbols. Symbols may appear more than once. Sarah has made four attempts, and her accuracy is shown below. What is the code? (Note – one symbol appears more than once in the correct code).

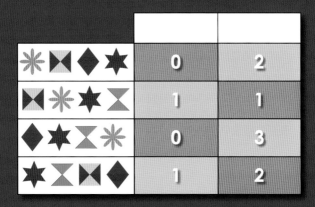

TWO MINUTE

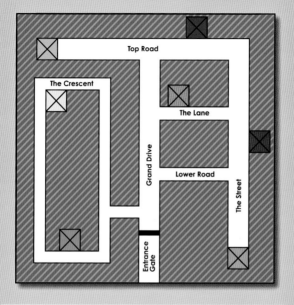

S ally delivers newspapers to eight houses in a
neighborhood as shown. Her father drives her to the
neighborhood and parks somewhere past the entrance
gate while Sally walks around. Where should her father
not park in order to keep Sally's paper delivery round to a
minimum?

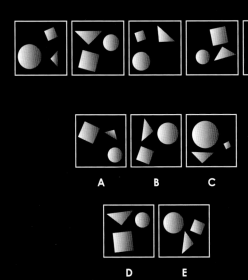

Choose one of the tiles to complete this sequence of shapes.

48

Can you continue this sequence?

1, 70, 2, 52, 3, 34, 4, 140, 5, ?

TWO MINUTE

Put these nine words into three groups of three words.

DOG

FOAL

GOAT

CAT

FOX

TAG

TOAD

LAX

COG

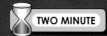

TWO MINUTE

= MOST EXPENSIVE

= 10c >

+ < $1.00

+ + = $2.80

+ + + + = $5.90

Red, orange, yellow and green peppers are all priced in units of 10 cents. They all have different prices within a range of 50 cents. From the information given, can you work out the price of each?

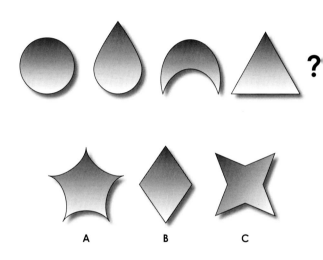

?

A   B   C

Can work out what the next shape will be!

52

Can you solve this dodecagon dilemma by identifying the missing number?

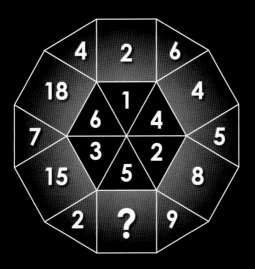

TWO MINUTE

The five football teams on the island of Boot play each other just once during the season. The current league table is shown. Can you work out the score between United and Athletic? (To start the ball rolling, check City's results).

	PLAYED	WON	DRAWN	LOST	GOALS FOR	GOALS AGAINST
UNITED	3	2	1	0	4	1
CITY	3	2	0	1	2	2
TOWN	3	1	2	0	4	3
RANGERS	2	0	1	1	3	4
ATHLETIC	3	0	0	3	1	4

TWO MINUTE

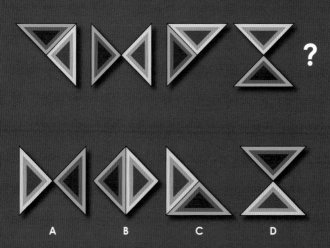

Which of the options shown continues this triangular sequence?

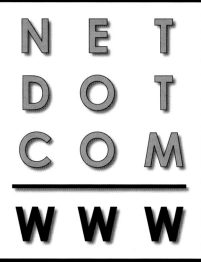

Using only numbers 1 to 8 to represent each of the symbols shown, add these symbols (which have descending value vertically) together, to give the total shown.

B eat the clock, and insert plus and minus signs to achieve the totals shown.

27   2   7   12   10   =   10

19   5   3   18   9   =   20

10   17   3   6   12   =   30

2   1   14   3   22   =   40

TWO MINUTE

Enter the numbers shown in the circles of the diagram so that each line always adds up to a total of 50.

3, 6, 12, 15, 17, 18, 21, 27, 30

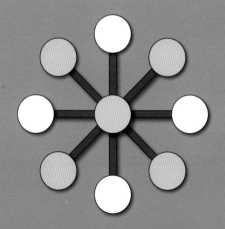

TWO MINUTE

THREE MINUTE PUZZLES

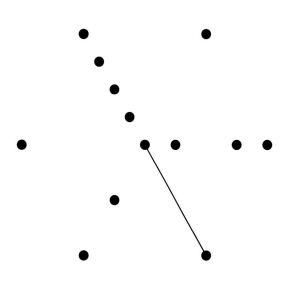

Connect a total of seven spots with eight more connecting lines to make a familiar shape.

7	4	3
5	O	6
9	2	6

4	2	O
5	5	2
O	9	7

O	5	6
2	O	8
9	4	O

O	4	O
7	4	6
O	5	O

?	7	O
2	O	6
?	5	O

O	?	?
5	9	7
?	O	?

THREE MINUTE

The National Lottery has balls numbered as shown previously. Four 1s appeared on the first four balls drawn. The six jackpot balls were rearranged in ascending numerical order, and none of the balls showing a 1 was next to another ball showing a 1. All five colors were represented, and the total of the six numbers was 106. What was the number shown on the second ball in the sequence?

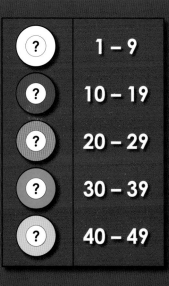

?	1 – 9
?	10 – 19
?	20 – 29
?	30 – 39
?	40 – 49

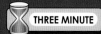

THREE MINUTE

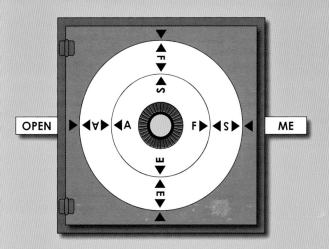

OPEN

ME

Hidden inside this safe is your inheritance. Can you rotate the two dials shown, while saying the magic words, to open it?

448
936
1424
1912
?

What should the next number in this sequence be?

Starting from the top left hand corner of the courtyard shown, a frog hops onto all of the paving stones, hopping from an adjacent paving stone to the next, without hopping onto the same paving stone twice. How many different ways could he do this, starting from the same paving stone?

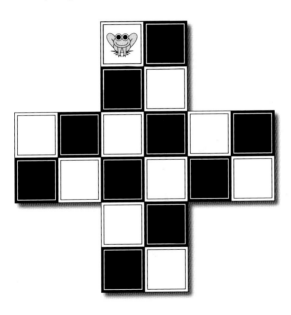

THREE MINUTE

Compete the grid by inserting the given numbers to determine the final total. Treat each calculation in sequence from left to right, e.g. a + b x c = (a + b) x c.

11, 12, 13, 14, 20, 23, 32, 33, 44, 81, 141, 152.

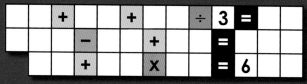

		+			+			÷	3	=		
		−			+					=		
		+			X				=	6		

| | | | 7 |

THREE MINUTE

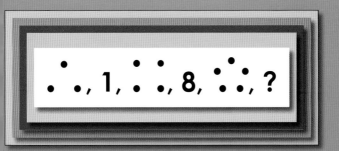

C an you work out what the next number in this sequence should be?

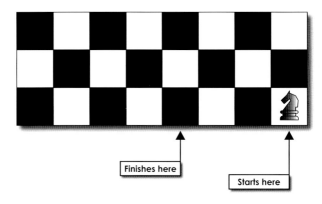

Finishes here

Starts here

In a chess game, the knight moves two squares forward in any direction and then one square sideways. Starting from the corner of the board, move the knight so that he lands only once on each of the squares shown, and f inishes in the highlighted square.

Can you complete the following set of twenty digits.

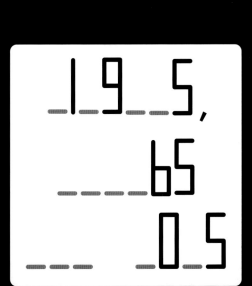

W here should the missing square be placed in the final box?

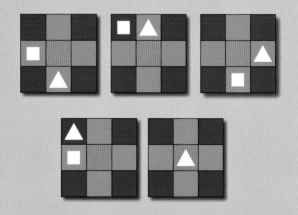

THREE MINUTE

This illustration shows two views of the same cube. Can you work out the missing number?

22	7	16	37
?			29
4			11
56	2	1	67

Work out the sequence used to create the numbered square shown and you will discover the missing number. (Note – once a square has a value displayed, it should be ignored).

Each letter represents a different value from 0 to 9, and these values are added together to give the answers shown. What is the value of 'LINES'?

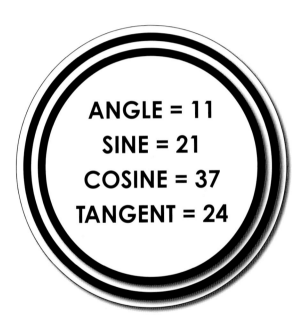

ANGLE = 11
SINE = 21
COSINE = 37
TANGENT = 24

THREE MINUTE

The following sequence uses just five colors – red, orange, yellow, green and blue. What should the next three colors in the sequence be?

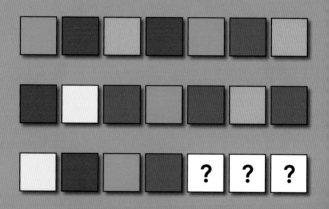

THREE MINUTE

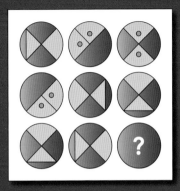

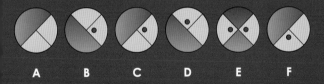

A B C D E F

Fill in the missing circle of this aquatic puzzle with one of the six watery options. Which one will complete the picture?

BIRDS FEEDING	TIME
6 – 12, A	0800 – 0900
12 – 18, AB	0900 – 1000
18 – 24, ABC	1000 –1100
12 – 18, AB	1100 – 1200
18 – 24, ABC	1200 – 1300
30, ALL	1300 – 1400
18 – 24, ABD	1400 – 1500
12 – 18, AD	1500 – 1600
6 – 12, A	1600 – 1700
6 – 12, A	1700 – 1800

There are 30 birds in the large aviary at the zoo and their feeding times are shown in this table. There are at least 6 birds of each type, and they all eat together. Currently there are 23 birds feeding. 1 hour and 20 minutes ago there was exactly the same number. In 42 minutes there will be 6 fewer. What is the time, and how many white gannets are there?

'X' marks the spot where the treasure is buried. Can you piece the map together to locate the elusive 'X'?

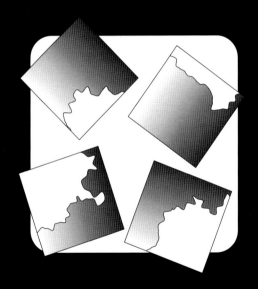

THREE MINUTE

Developers of a new neighborhood are planning the road layout. Each development within the neighborhood needs to be serviced by the road, which enters in Holly View and exits from Evergreen Climb. There is only enough road material to build the number of road sections shown, so where will you find the crossroads?

Entry	Holly View	Acacia Avenue	Beech Crescent
	Oaklands	Birch Rise	Cherry Tree
	Forest Hill	Cedar Way	Evergreen Climb	Exit
	Rowan Street	Woodlands	Sycamore Lane

= 10

= 1

= 1

THREE MINUTE

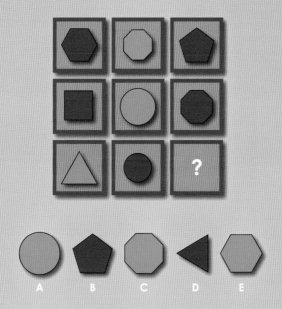

Which one of the shapes shown should replace the question mark in this puzzle?

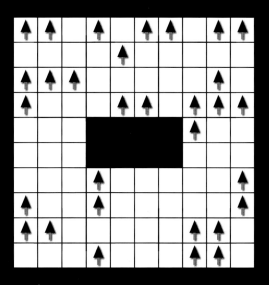

Lord Snodgrass is planning to build a gamekeeper's cottage in his pine forest. Following the sequence in the layout of the trees, can you work out how many trees need to be cut down in order to build the cottage?

Fill in the magic square with the numbers 5 to 20, so that all the columns, rows and diagonals add up to 50. In addition, each group of four squares which make up any other square inside the grid needs to add up to 50 as well.

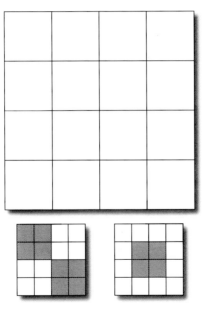

Which of the options shown will balance the fifth equation?

A B C D E

THREE MINUTE

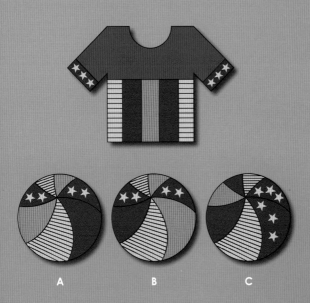

A   B   C

The Lagoon netball team have designed their shirts to match the colorful netball they play with. Which of the three balls belongs to them?

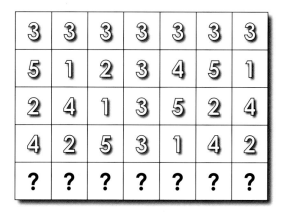

3	3	3	3	3	3	3
5	1	2	3	4	5	1
2	4	1	3	5	2	4
4	2	5	3	1	4	2
?	?	?	?	?	?	?

Continue this numerical sequence. (Note – no figure higher than a 5 can be used).

Divide this box by three poker-straight lines. Each section should contain three diamonds, three clubs and three spades.

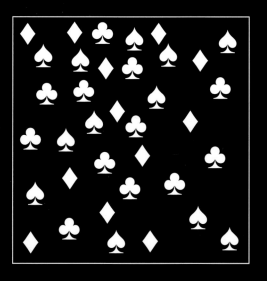

THREE MINUTE

Place a three-digit number in each of the empty circles so that each side of the octagon always adds up to a total of 1427.

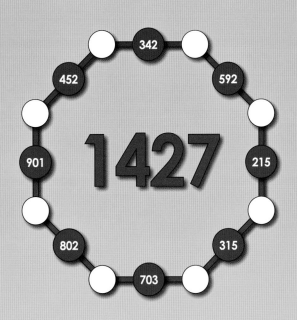

THREE MINUTE

ONE MINUTE PUZZLES

Page 8
The answer is E.

Page 9
4, 5, 6, 7, 8 is the only set of consecutive digits whose total is divisible by 6, so Player Smith's shirt number is 5.

Page 10
A dodecagon, or regular 12-sided polygon.

Page 11
The answer is D because each triangle's color runs through red, yellow, blue, green sequence and there are 'diamonds' of each color in the middle.

Page 12
The answer is 6. Running down the columns vertically, the numbers go

up by increments of 2, 3, 4, and 5.

Page 13
The numbers in the top left-hand corner increase in increments of 17, numbers in the top right increase in increments of 21, bottom left in increments of 25. Each time, the increments increase by four, so the hidden numbers must be increments of 29, and their values are 54, 83, and 112.

Page 14
The answer is A, because in the second clock, the number 1 moves round anticlockwise one place and the other numbers move away from the original position by 1 place each time. In the third clock, the number 1 again moves one place anticlockwise and the other numbers move by two places this time, and so on.

Page 15

Page 16

SOLUTIONS

Page 17

Each figure is half a playing card symbol turned upside down, so the fourth figure should be half of an upside down heart.

Page 18

The answer is C. Ignoring colors, each bar moves one space to the right each time, with the end bar returning to the left-hand side. At the same time, each color moves to the next highest bar each time, and moves from the highest bar back to the lowest.

Page 19

The answer is D, because all the others stay the same shape even when turned upside down.

Page 20

Adding a toothpick means that an eighth one has been added and shows the fraction 'one-ninth'.

Page 21

The missing numbers are as follows.

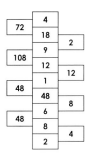

Page 22

The answer is B, as they are all views of a colored pyramid from the top, one side, beneath, and then the other side.

Page 23

10, 11, 12, 13, 14 is the sequence of numbers on the cars, so Car X's number is 10.

Page 24

Page 25

The answer is Quentin, because the initial letter of the names moves backwards through the alphabet.

Page 26

The answer is C, because all the

other spouts face to the right and that one faces to the left.

Page 27

The answer is 31. The only possible solutions are 1, 4, 13, 22, 31, 41; or 2, 4, 13, 22, 31, 42; or 3, 4, 13, 22, 31, 43.

Page 28

Page 29

The answer is B, because each shape is folded along the line and then rotated 90 degrees clockwise.

Page 30

Starting from the middle, the numbers follow an anticlockwise path and the values of each square go up in increments of two each time, so the missing square contains 2 ▲ and 1 ✹.

Page 31

The 'X' indicates 'GOAT' and 'Y' indicates 'PIG'.

Page 32

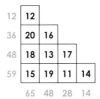

12	12			
36	20	16		
48	18	13	17	
59	15	19	11	14
	65	48	28	14

Page 33

7	2	6	4	8
2	3	5	1	6
6	5	4	9	7
4	1	9	2	3
8	6	7	3	4

Page 34

The answer is D, as the window is rotated 90 degrees clockwise each time.

TWO MINUTE PUZZLES

Page 36

E and F, because each of the other pairs of identical shapes can be joined together to form a square.

Page 37

The answer is C, because the shape rotates 90 degrees anticlockwise each time, while at the same time the top left-hand block is removed.

SOLUTIONS

Page 38

The answer is two.

Page 39

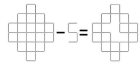

Page 40

Page 41

The answer is 8, because each external number is the sum of the two nearest internal numbers minus the opposite internal number.

Page 42

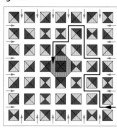

Page 43

The answer is B.

Page 44

The answer is 70. The sequence shows the total of the possible announced scores during one game of tennis, before the game is over or deuce is reached.

Page 45

The sum of the numbers shown is 2001, so the film title represented is '2001: A Space Odyssey'.

Page 46

Page 47

He should park anywhere but in the shaded gray area.

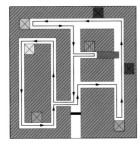

Page 48

The answer is D, because the triangle in each box alternates between pointing to a circle and then pointing to a square.

Page 49

The answer is 62. Each of the digits 1, 2, 3, 4 is followed by the number of distinct straight lines and then the number of curved lines that is needed to make up that number (e.g. 1 has 7 straight and 0 curved lines; 2 has 5 straight and 2 curved lines; etc.).

Page 50

In each group, the first two words have the common letter removed and their remaining letters are used to form the letters of the third word.

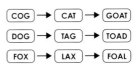

COG → CAT → GOAT

DOG → TAG → TOAD

FOX → LAX → FOAL

Page 51

Red + Yellow + Green = $2.80. Therefore R = $0.90, G = $0.80, Y= $1.10. Y + Y + Y + O + O = $5.90, therefore O = $1.30.

Page 52

The number of points in each shape goes up by one each time from zero, so the answer is B because it has four points.

Page 53

The answer is 35. The number in each square is the difference between its two touching external triangles multiplied by its touching internal triangle, e.g. 35 = (9 − 2) x 5.

Page 54

Win = 3pts, Draw = 2pts, Lose = 0pts. City won two games 1:0, which must have been against Rangers and Athletic. City lost their other game 2:0. Rangers' other game must have been a 3:3 draw with Town. Town therefore drew 0:0 with United, and won their other game 1:0 against Athletic. City must have lost 2:0 to United. United therefore beat Athletic 2:1.

Page 55

The answer is C, because first the blue triangle moves 90 degrees anticlockwise, then the yellow triangle, then the blue triangle, and so on.

Page 56

```
 3  8  6
 2  4  6
 1  4  5
─────────
 7  7  7
```

Page 57

$$27 - 2 + 7 - 12 - 10 = 10$$
$$19 - 5 - 3 + 18 - 9 = 20$$
$$10 + 17 - 3 - 6 + 12 = 30$$
$$2 - 1 + 14 + 3 + 22 = 40$$

Page 58

THREE MINUTE PUZZLES

Page 60

Page 61

The 0s correspond to the positions of the spots on each side of a die, so each question mark has to be filled with an 0.

Page 62

The answer is 3. The first and third balls must be 1 and 11. The fifth or sixth ball must be 31 or 41 respectively. Pink cannot be 22, or the total of 106 will be exceeded, therefore the pink ball must be 20. Green and yellow can only add up to 71, so will be 31/40 or 30/41. 1 + 11 + 20 + 71 = 103. Plus 3 = 106.

Page 63

Rotate the dials to line up the words 'Open Sesame'.

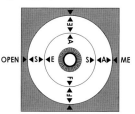

Page 64

24:00. The numbers are all times on a 24-hour clock and the times shown are all fifths of a day.

Page 65

There are seven different ways.

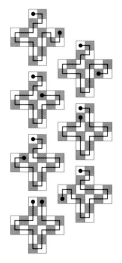

Page 68

7	10	13	18	21	4	1	16
12	19	8	5	14	17	22	3
9	6	11	20	23	2	15	

Page 69

The twenty digits are 'fingers, thumbs and toes'.

Page 70

Bottom right hand corner. The triangle circles the square in an anticlockwise direction, moving around one space each time.

Page 71

From the illustration, R + 9, B – G = 4, G – Y = 3, B – Y = 7. We require R + B – Y, which equals 9 + 7 = 16. Therefore the answer is 16.

Page 72

The answer is 46. Starting with an empty grid, start with 1 as shown, then miss 0 squares and display 2. Miss 1 square (3) and display 4. Miss 2 squares (5 and 6) and display 7. Miss 3 squares (8, 9 and 10) and display 11. Miss 4 squares (12, 13, 14, and 15) and display 16, etc.

Page 73

The answer is 21. From COSINE and

Page 66

The answer is 817.

1	1	+	2	0	+	3	2	÷	3	=	2	1
1	4	1	–	1	2	+	2	3	=	1	5	2
	1	3	+	3	3	×	1	4	=	6	4	4

8	1	7

Page 67

The answer is 35, which is the number of triangles that can be found within each shape when all the dots are joined up.

SINE, C + O = 16 so must be 7 + 9. SINE must therefore be 2, 5, 6, and 8. ANGLE = 11, therefore N and E must be 2 and 5. A + G + L = 4. From TANGENT and ANGLE, 2T + N − L = 13. T = 4, N = 5 and L = 0. LINES is therefore 21.

Page 74

The answer is orange, blue and yellow. Red is used for the powers of two. Green and orange are used alternately for the remaining prime numbers. Blue is used for the remaining even numbers. Yellow is used for the remaining odd numbers.

Page 75

The answer is E, which will complete the series of the heads and tails of a school of fish.

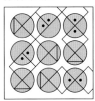

Page 76

The time is 14.17 and there are 10 white gannets.

Only 14.00–15.00 satisfies all time requirements. In order to move into the other time zones given, the time must be 14.17. Using the first letter of the birds' names, G + L + D = 23 = G + L + T. Therefore L = T = N. But G + L + D + T = 30. Therefore T = 7 (30 − 23 = L). Between 15.00 and 16.00 there are 6 fewer than 23 birds feeding, i.e. G + T = 17. Therefore G = 10 (17 − 7).

Page 77

The 'X' that marks the spot is to be found at the intersection of the 'X' formed where the four pieces meet when connected.

Page 78

The only possible route is shown and the crossroads will occur in Birch Rise.

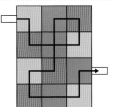

Page 79

The answer is E, because the initial

letters of the names of all the shapes shown spell out the word 'Hopscotch' when read from left to right along each row.

Page 80

The answer is one. The sequence runs in a spiral pattern that is two dots – space one dot – space. This cycle is repeated, but in each cycle the number of spaces is increased by one.

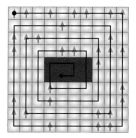

Page 81

8	9	14	19
13	20	7	10
11	6	17	16
18	15	12	5

Page 82

The answer is C.

Page 83

The answer is C, because the pattern sequence that runs across the shirt from right to left, including the sleeves, is repeated clockwise on the correct ball.

Page 84

The central (fourth) figure, 3, remains static each time. The third and fifth figures move down one and up one respectively each time. The second and sixth figures move down two and up two respectively each time. And the first and seventh figures move down three and up three each time.

Page 85

Page 86

LAGOON
BOOKS

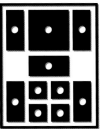